Contents

Published 2011. Pedigree Books Ltd, Beech Hill House, Walnut Gardens, Exeter, Devon EX4 4DH. books@pedigreegroup.co.uk | www.pedigreebooks.com

nickelodeon

Pedigree

PRESTIGIOUS!
♡ iCarly

TO: LLY
FROM: JOHN   CHRISTMAS 2019

£7.99

Carly

👤 Profile ▼

is browsing in 'Build-a-Bra' edit

▼ Personal Info:

Full name:	Carlotta Shay
Birthday:	January 14th
Star Sign:	Capricorn
Hair Colour:	Brown
Eye Colour:	Brown
Carly likes: 👍	Cupcakes, my BFF Sam, gummy bears
Carly dislikes: 👎	Homework, bugs, iCarly.com haters like Nevel, cold showers

SplashFace

Carly has 1,031 SplashFace Supporters, scroll down to view more:

1,031 friends   See All

Freddie Benson

Gibby Gibson

Sam Puckett

Spencer Shay

Suprising SplashFace Fact: x

I absolutely believe in Bigfoot! Oh yeah, you've got to love a yeti!

👤 Latest Wall Posts

Freddie:
Hey, Carly. What time are we filming tomorrow? It's the annual general meeting of the AV club after school and I'm up for President again. Don't want to miss the vote!

Spencer:
Wassup Sis, check out the link on my page to my latest piece of artwork – it's made entirely from fluff I found down the back of the sofa!

Sam:
Wanna come over and hang out? My mum says she'll pick you up, but she doesn't have a licence right now so you'd better ask Spencer if he'll drive you.

Mandy:
OMG! I can't believe I'm actually friends with Carly from iCarly – I love iCarly, I love iCarly, I love iCarly, I love iCarly, I love iCarly…

Sam:
Ignore that last post, I'm coming over to you. My fridge is like, totally bare. You got any meat?

Carly:
Sure. I got some fat cakes too.

Sam:
I'll be there in 5, 4, 3, 2…

Draw or stick in your own profile picture **and write your** name and comment.

Lily:

Hello Carly, I do not get how in 8 years you have not aged yet your actress must have

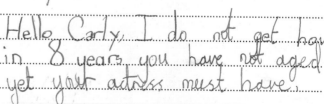

Lewbert's Letter Link

Lewbert detests being a doorman at Bushwell Plaza and he especially hates mopping the lobby! He'd much rather be in his back office with his feet up, drinking a skinny latte whilst working through a crossword. Can you use the clues to fill in the blanks in this iCarly crossword puzzle? When you've completed the letter square, scan down the red column to reveal another unsavoury character from the show.

1. Freddie's surname.
2. Sword-based sport enjoyed by Spencer and Freddie.
3. The first name of Carly's father.
4. Lewbert's last name.
5. Spencer once bought a Proton Cruiser, thinking it was a prop from this show.
6. The type of artwork that Spencer creates.
7. Wacky style of dancing featured on the iCarly show.
8. Sam's mum's first name.
9. The second name in Carly's Bushwell apartment block.
10. Obnoxious and rude competitor on 'America Sings'.
11. Ted Franklin's job at Carly, Sam and Freddie's high school.
12. The fruity drinks that Carly loves to sip.
13. The meaty sauce that inspires Sam's favourite colour.
14. The name of iCarly's crazed number one fan.

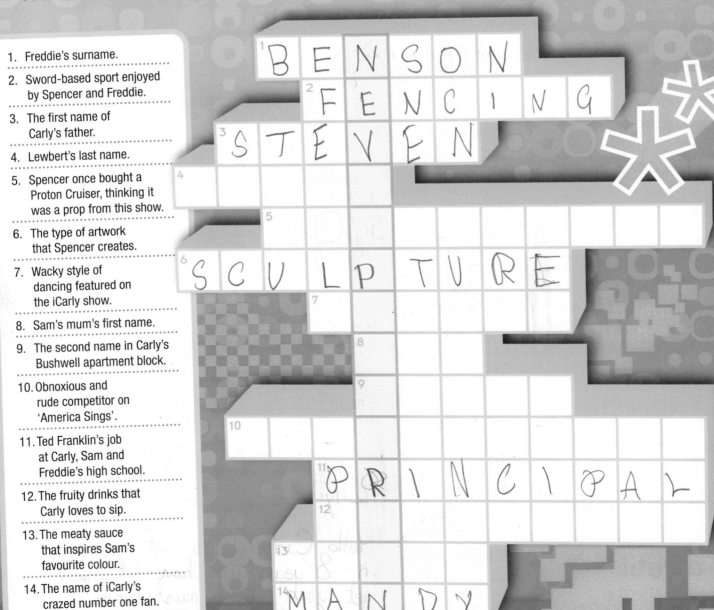

Puckett's Prankster Kit

If, like Sam, you have more than a passing interest in pranks, you need a treasure chest of tools to help you achieve maximum hilarity from your practical jokes! Why not make your own handy, portable kit packed with everything you'll need to keep your friends, family and enemies slipping, sliding, screaming and generally looking silly.

THE TRICKS:

THE KIT:

- One empty shoe box plus lid
- Old magazines
- Paper glue
- Felt-tip pens

Decorate the shoe box with pictures of your favourite iCarly characters – you could either cut pictures out of magazines and stick them on or draw your own designs. Take your time decorating the box to make it look as funky and fashion forward as possible, this will detract attention from what really lurks within.

PACKING YOUR KIT

If you're an established joker you may already have some shop-bought equipment, but if not you can get started with the following:

- Some deflated balloons (great for making unpleasant noises and/or water bombs)
- One feather
- Umbrella
- A £1 or £2 coin
- Sticky tape
- A reel of fine white cotton

- A small tin of sweetcorn, a bag of diced carrot, one small can of chicken soup, one small pot yoghurt (the perfect mix for instant fake vomit.)
- One can of string cheese or squirty cream

1. Tape a strand of cotton to the coin and then place it on the pavement. Hide nearby and hold the other end of the cotton. When someone tries to pick up the money, yank the string! Are they greedy enough to try again? For added fun, try gluing a coin to the floor and watching passers by scrabble to pick it up.

2. Wait until someone falls fast asleep on the sofa, squirt cheese into their hand and simultaneously tickle their nose with a feather. Now hide! The dozer is bound to scratch their nose with their cheesy hand and get a face full.

3. Take a folded umbrella, fill it with lots of pieces of cut up paper and then put it back where you found it. When the person opens the brolly they get showered as if they were in a snow storm!

PUT IT TO THE TEST!

Are you crazy about Carly, Sam and Freddie? Do you find yourself ordering spaghetti tacos in restaurants, or logging on to SplashFace every time you surf the net? If so, this cool tick test should be a total synch! All the quiz questions have been devised by the show's toughest puzzle plotters to test your knowledge of iCarly.com. Find a pen or pencil, then give it a try!

1. Freddie once wore pink shorts to play tennis because...

- [x] a. Sam put a red sock in the wash to make him think he was having bad luck.
- [ ] b. His mum just loves him in pink.
- [ ] c. He couldn't find any of his own so had to borrow a pair of Carly's.

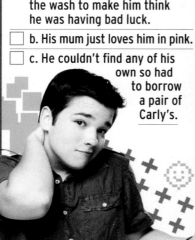

2. Carly suffers mildly with...

- [ ] a. Agoraphobia – a fear of open spaces.
- [ ] b. Aquaphobia – a fear of water.
- [x] c. Claustrophobia – a fear of enclosed spaces.

3. Freddie's mum was pregnant with him for...

- [ ] a. 9 months.
- [x] b. 10 months.
- [x] c. 11 months.

4. When Spencer wants to predict the future he turns for advice to his...

- [ ] a. Magic eight-ball.
- [x] b. Magic meatball.
- [ ] c. Magic football.

5. Before becoming Carly's doorman, Lewbert was once...

- [ ] a. A warty witch in a spooky theme park.
- [ ] b. A circus freak.
- [x] c. A male model.

6. Gibby is called Gibby because...

- [ ] a. He looks like a Gibbon.
- [ ] b. He likes singing like the Gibb brothers from the Bee Gees.
- [x] c. His surname is Gibson.

7. According to Sam, she only kissed Freddie because...

- [ ] a. She was pretending to be her twin sister Melanie.
- [x] b. She could stop stressing over never having kissed anyone.
- [ ] c. She was trying to be sick in his mouth.

8. Carly and Freddie are sometimes known as...

- [x] a. Creddie.
- [ ] b. Frarly.
- [ ] c. CarFred.

9. Sam's list of favourite things in life includes...

- [ ] a. Stripy T-shirts.
- [x] b. Fat Cakes.
- [ ] c. Diet fizzy soda.

10. Which of these has not formed the basis of a Spencer sculpture?

- [x] a. A pile of yo-yos.
- [ ] b. A fan of hammers.
- [ ] c. A mound of Marmite.

11. Carly, Sam and Freddie attend...

- [ ] a. Bushwell High School.
- [x] b. Ridgeway High School.
- [ ] c. Seattle State High School.

12. Carly's rival Nevel has a review website called...

- [x] a. Nevelocity.
- [ ] b. Nevel say Never.
- [ ] c. Nev Says.com.

13. Which of these things does Ms Briggs have hidden in her locker?

- [ ] a. A collection of gymnastics trophies.
- [ ] b. A pile of lemons.
- [x] c. A life-size cardboard cut out of singer Randy Jackson.

14. Sam hates the word...

- [x] a. Panties.
- [ ] b. Orang-utan.
- [ ] c. Howdy.

15. To win the enormous school locker #239 Sam, Freddie, Carly and Gibby had to guess the number of Fat Cakes in a big glass cylinder. How many were in there?

- [x] a. 2,718.
- [ ] b. 5.
- [ ] c. 1,827.

16. Which of these has not been featured on a Penny Tee...

- [x] a. Cheese Police.
- [ ] b. Random Sass.
- [ ] c. I Heart Porcupines.

17. Carly's father Steven Shay is...

- [x] a. Stationed on a submarine.
- [ ] b. Trekking in Patagonia.
- [ ] c. In jail for computer hacking.

18. Nevel's ultimate life goal is to...

- [x] a. Marry Carly and move to the country.
- [ ] b. Review big A-listers instead of pathetic webshows.
- [ ] c. Open a haberdashery store.

19. Spencer once faked his own death because...

- [ ] a. Freddie's mum decided she wanted to marry him.
- [x] b. He realised many artists only achieve real fame and success after death.
- [ ] c. He had spent all the rent money on buying Galaxy War props.

20. T-Bo's speciality at the Groovy Smoothie is...

- [ ] a. Food on a stick.
- [ ] b. Smoothies in mugs.
- [ ] c. T-Bone steaks.

LOGO A GO-GO

Galini's Pie Shop makes the best pies on the planet — the iCarly gang can't get enough of them! Old Mr Galini has sadly passed away, but luckily his grandaughter Trudy has decided to shelve her acting ambitions and keep the family business alive.

TO KEEP CUSTOM ROLLING IN, TRUDY WANTS TO UPDATE THE PIE SHOP SIGN AND REBRAND THE STORE. CAN YOU HELP HER DESIGN A DAZZLING NEW LOGO? SKETCH YOUR IDEAS IN THE FRAME BELOW, THEN COLOUR THE BEST ONE IN USING ATTENTION-GRABBING FELT-TIPS.

GALINI'S PIE SHOP

IF YOU ENJOYED THAT, WHY NOT HAVE A GO AT CREATING NEW SIGNS FOR THESE ICARLY DESTINATIONS TOO?

The Groovy Smoothie

Build-A-Bra

The Cheesecake Warehouse

DIGITAL DAYS

Got tons of photos stored on your computer or on the memory stick of your digital camera? Don't keep them squirrelled away in there forever! Here are some fab ways to put your store of snaps to good use.

CREATE A COLLAGE

Collages let you showcase loads of shots without having to use too many frames or too much wall space. Just print your favourite photos onto photographic white paper and then cut round them to make interesting shapes. Stick the pictures onto a large sheet of stiff card, allowing the edges to overlap. You could either prop this up as it is, or mount it in a clip-frame. If the collage is going to be a gift, you could also ask the people featured in the photos to write down notes and memories to stick in amongst the poses.

CLEVER CARDS

Photo cards make things so much more personal! Instead of buying a boring old shop-bought greetings card, create your own using white board, felt tips, glue and your fave photo. Don't forget to add a funny caption underneath.

KEEPSAKE BOX

Digital photos can be used to make a really special gift for your best friend. Find a large shoe box with a lid and then decorate it with photographs of the pair of you. Stick a flittering of glitter over the top and then cover the card with sticky back plastic to keep the pictures protected.

POCKET MONEY POSSIBILITIES...

BFF
Many gift companies can now personalise objects with your photos. Why not save up your pocket money and get your BFF's face printed on a coaster or a calendar? That way you'll be able to remember your friends every single day.

Photo fashion
Customise your clothing! You could choose a photo of your family celebrating Christmas to adorn a long-sleeved winter top, or a fab holiday snap on a bright T-shirt.

What a mug
Let someone you love enjoy a memorable cuppa every morning by having a special photo transferred on to a plain white coffee mug.

IF YOU MUST LEAVE YOUR SHOTS ON YOUR COMPUTER, AT LEAST LET THEM SHINE ON-SCREEN. CHANGE THE WALLPAPER ON YOUR DESKTOP TO FEATURE ONE OF YOUR FAVOURITE SNAPS.

Comedy CAPTIONS

20 iC 11

iCARLY

Gibby was thinking ____

Sam ____

I love my brother Spencer because ____

CARLY'S BEEN GOING THROUGH HER BOX OF PHOTOS!
SHE HAS FOUND SOME CLASSIC SHOTS OF HER FRIENDS,
BUT SHE HASN'T HAD TIME TO LABEL THEM. CAN YOU HELP
HER OUT? LOOK AT EACH PIC AND THEN TRY AND COME
UP WITH THE FUNNIEST CAPTION YOU CAN THINK OF.

What a surprise, _____

_____

Me with my _____

_____

Can you believe _____

_____

This was taken when _____

_____

Sam Puckett

Profile ▼

is knee deep in a bucket of fried chicken

▼ Personal Info:

Full name:	Samantha Puckett
Birthday:	April 17th
Star Sign:	Aries
Hair Colour:	Blonde
Eye Colour:	Blue
Sam likes: 👍	Gross-out videos, pretty much anything edible, bunking off school
Sam dislikes: 👎	Hairy armpits, my vomit-inducing perfect twin Melanie, stripy shirts

TTYL

To Sam!

Sam has 901 SplashFace Supporters, scroll down to view more

901 friends   See All

Carly Shay

Gibby Gibson

Freddie Benson

Spencer Shay

Surprising SplashFace Fact: ✕

She loves meat – but doesn't mind a salad!

Latest Wall Posts

Freddie:
Sam, have you been messing with the brakes on my bike again? I fell into a hedge this morning.

Sam:
LOL! 😊

Freddie:
So not funny! I have a black eye and my mum is making me wear a pirate patch.

Sam:
Again. LOL! 😄

Spencer:
I'm overdue returning my DVD again, can you help me? I'm going to say I got trapped under a sofa…

Sam:
Sure. But did you know that Seattle PD has introduced prison sentences for unlawful DVD borrowing?

Spencer:
Really?

Sam:
No, I lied.

Spencer:
Oooh, you're good! I totally fell for that.

Draw or stick in your own profile picture **and write your** name and comment.

Lily:
Ooh! Nice, Sam!

STYLISH DOWN TO A TEE

The iCarly team love Penny Tees! Penny is the talented sister of Spencer's best friend Socko and she's been running a bespoke T-shirt design company for years.

You can always pick out a Penny Tee — it has a different coloured hem on one sleeve and a little penny coin on the side. A Penny Tee wouldn't be a Penny Tee without the quirkiest of slogans. Can you design a few of your own on the blank prototypes below? Colour the T-shirts in cool shades and then emblazon your message in big letters!

FANTABULOUS FIVE!

Need a shot of artistic inspiration? Here are the gang's five fave Penny Tee slogans to get you started. Can you guess who wore each one?

A. MY CHEESE, MY RULES

_____

B. WICKED TWITCH

_____

C. SQUIRREL GERMS

_____

D. POODLE JUICE

_____

E. BUTTER ME QUEASY

_____

iWant My Website Back

IT'S FUNNY HOW A LITTLE THING LIKE SPENCER'S NEW CREDIT CARD COULD WREAK CHAOS AND DESTRUCTION FOR THE iCARLY GANG...

"Next Sam will add two cups of chopped chicken," explained Carly.

Her best friend smiled sweetly and then waved a wooden spoon – the pair were filming a knockout cookery segment for the iCarly show!

Freddie panned the webcam back to reveal an expanse of baby blue porcelain.

"That's right," nodded Sam. "That's how you make "Chicken Soup in a Toilet!"

Carly grinned. She wasn't sure why exactly they'd decided it would be fun to make a batch of soup in a lavatory, but she was mighty glad that they'd given it a whirl!

Sam hit the applause

cam and then the girls wound up the show.

"And we're clear!" announced Freddie, flicking the LIVE light off.

Just as the gang were shutting down the laptops, Spencer burst into the loft.

"So..." he beamed. "Who wants to go out to dinner to break in my fancy new credit card?"

While Sam fetched her coat, Carly looked confused.

"Why have you got a new card?"

MY NEW CARD HAS GOT A BUNNY HOLOGRAM!

"I tried to order two new special pillows online, but the company declined my credit card," jabbered Spencer. "So I called to complain and I got in a fight with the credit card lady..."

"How long does this story go on?" butted in Carly.

"Oh, it gets better!" grinned Spencer. "I ended up cancelling that credit card and ordered a new one so I could buy my pillows. And guess what? My new card has got a bunny hologram!"

Carly bundled her brother out of the door. Much as she was enjoying discussing Spencer's banking arrangements, she seriously needed some dinner.

Carly shook her head. They both knew the password had always been 'Samlovesham.'

Freddie tapped a few buttons, then hit a bunch more. How could the tech producer be locked out of his own show?

"It says 'Unable to charge renewal fee. Account closed'," gasped Freddie. "We don't own iCarly anymore!"

"But it automatically charges Spencer's credit card every…" Carly's voice trailed into silence. Spencer had cancelled that credit card!

The pair freaked out.

"All right! Don't panic!" screeched Carly, totally panicking. "J-just buy it back!"

Freddie was already onto it, but it seemed that someone else had bought it first.

"It says the url belongs to someone called Amanda Valdez."

Carly clicked on the profile picture and screamed. It was Mandy – iCarly's insane, biggest fan!

"Calm down," soothed Freddie. "At least the site was bought by someone we know."

"Oh yeah!" snapped Carly. "Someone who's a lunatic and wears a duck mask!"

Yep, iCarly.com had a problem on its hands. The gang's precious url had been hijacked by a psychotic she-duck.

After school the next day, Freddie was hanging out at Carly's place.

"How many people watched iCarly last night?" wondered Carly, wandering up to the computer.

Freddie tried to log on.

"It won't let me get into our account," he frowned. "Did you change our password?"

iWant My Website Back

Mandy Valdez elbowed her way to the best seat in the Groovy Smoothie. The iCarly team had asked for a meeting and the excitement was getting all too much!

"Have you seen Carly, Sam and-or Freddie?" she barked, shoving some innocent Smoothie sippers out of the way. "No? Your loss!"

When her heroes finally walked through the door, Mandy nearly collapsed with joy.

"Hey, you guys!" she bellowed, dragging each one into an inappropriately-tight bear hug.

"Mandy," smiled Carly, trying to be nice. "You got taller."

Sam rolled her eyes. "And louder."

"And stronger," groaned Freddie.

"Have you missed me?" beamed Mandy. "Look, I got a special iCarly hat!"

Mandy pulled a garish purple hat out of her rucksack. Sam winced when she noticed that it was fitted with a screen that flashed up pictures of iCarly screengrabs. Seriously weird!

Freddie cut to the chase.

"Thanks for buying iCarly.com when it expired," he said. "If you'll just sign this transfer document, you won't have to worry about it any more."

Mandy giggled. "No way!"

"You won't sign the url back over to us?" gasped Carly.

"You guys almost lost it!" guffawed Mandy. "I can hang on to it and be like your manager!"

Carly and Freddie nearly fell off their stools.

"You what?" spat Sam.

"Good news, huh?" smiled Mandy.

"Ooo! And I've got a new duck mask to show you, too."

BFF

A few depressing days' later, the gang got ready to film the next webisode of iCarly under the guiding eye of their duck-loving manager. Spencer was chilling out downstairs when the buzzer went.

"You order some pillows from pillow-my-head.com?" asked a Sendex Delivery man.

Spencer nodded and then scribbled his name on the man's clipboard.

"I am so psyched to be getting these!" he grinned. "So where are my pillows?"

The Sendex guy pointed to the apartment elevator. The doors slid open, revealing a wall of pillows.

"Whoa…" gasped Spencer. "I just ordered two!"

"Nope," the Sendex guy replied. "You ordered 200 pillows."

The man flipped the clipboard round to show that Spencer had not only ordered them, he'd signed for them too.

There was a loud grunt as a second delivery man crashed out of the elevator, tumbling through the wall of bedding.

I AM SO PSYCHED TO BE GETTING THESE!

If the Sendex guys were feeling reasonable, they should have taken 198 pillows back. Unfortunately they weren't in that kind of mood today.

"No, no, no, no!" yelled Spencer, landing himself in the biggest pillow fight he'd had since fifth grade.

Things weren't going much better in the studio upstairs. Working with Mandy was proving to be a nightmare! The iCarly fan kept interrupting clips and knocking Freddie's camera.

"Mandy!" begged Carly. "We're in the middle of the show."

"OK," snivelled Mandy. "But some of Sam's hair is sticking out. Here…" Mandy pulled out a big pair of scissors and then snipped off the offending lock.

"I'm going to kill her," seethed Sam. It was time for iCarly to sign off.

"Please join us next time!" squeaked Carly, struggling to keep her best friend restrained.

When Mandy put on her duck mask for the closing credits, Sam went a funny shade of purple.

"I'm going to KILL her!"

After a 24 hour cooldown period, Carly and her friends had the strength to meet Mandy again at the Groovy Smoothie.

"Listen Mandy," began Freddie. "You've been so helpful to our show."

Carly nodded enthusiastically. "It's just that we'd feel more comfortable if you'd sign the iCarly.com url back over to us."

Mandy sipped her smoothie and nodded.

"I already gave it back," she shrugged. "Freddie emailed me last night begging for it. You're FreddieB123splashface.com, right?"

Freddie's face went white. "No."

"So who did I sign the website over to?" shrugged Mandy.

Freddie grabbed his backpack and dragged out his laptop. Sam shot daggers at Mandy, as the iCarly.com website address flashed up on the browser.

"No!" wailed Carly.

The regular, completely awesome iCarly site had been replaced by a naff homepage filled with the smug, smiling face of Nevel Papperman!

"Hello former iCarly fans!" he sneered. "Welcome to the new iCarly.com!"

The creep held up two grotesque puppets of Carly and Sam. What was Nevel doing? Even Groovy Smoothie waiter T-Bo stopped selling bagels on a stick so he could gawp at the cringy display on screen.

Nevel made the puppets parade like nubs across the screen, before shoving his hands underneath his arms.

"Carly and Sam are going to visit my underarms!" he smirked, beside himself with joy. "They can't breathe!!"

iWant My Website Back

Spencer was whiling away the afternoon hooking pillows with his fishing rod when Carly and the gang stormed into the apartment. Mandy followed behind like a nasty smell.

"That little nub-munch took our website down and then put on a puppet show making fun of us!" snarled Sam.

Carly nodded furiously. "And he made our puppet personas smell his pits!"

"Why's that little jerk always trying so hard to mess with you guys?" wondered Spencer.

Carly sighed. Nevel Papperman still hated her because she refused to kiss him, but really, who would pucker up to a creep like that?

"Hey! I know how to get the url back from Nevel!" insisted Mandy. "But first we're going to need three zebras…"

It was the last straw for Sam. She grabbed her biggest fan by the ear and dragged her into the kitchen.

he wasn't – instead he was promoting another autograph signing event for his fans.

"He's so conceited," groaned the producer.

WE'RE GOING TO NEED THREE ZEBRAS

While Puckett kept Mandy out of the way, Freddie logged on to find out if Nevel was saying more bad stuff about iCarly. For once

"This time he's in the lobby of the Beverly Garvin Hotel."

"Right!" announced Carly. "What if we show up there and trick Nevel into signing iCarly.com back to us?"

Sam and Freddie shrugged. It was a great plan with a fatal flaw – as soon as Papperman spotted them he'd know something was up!

"We could send Mandy?" suggested Freddie.

Sam rolled her eyes. "What about Spencer?"

"Nevel's seen Spencer too," replied Freddie.

Spencer dropped his fishing rod and strolled over to the computer. Carly started to grin.

"Maybe," she whispered. "But he hasn't met my great Aunt Natalie."

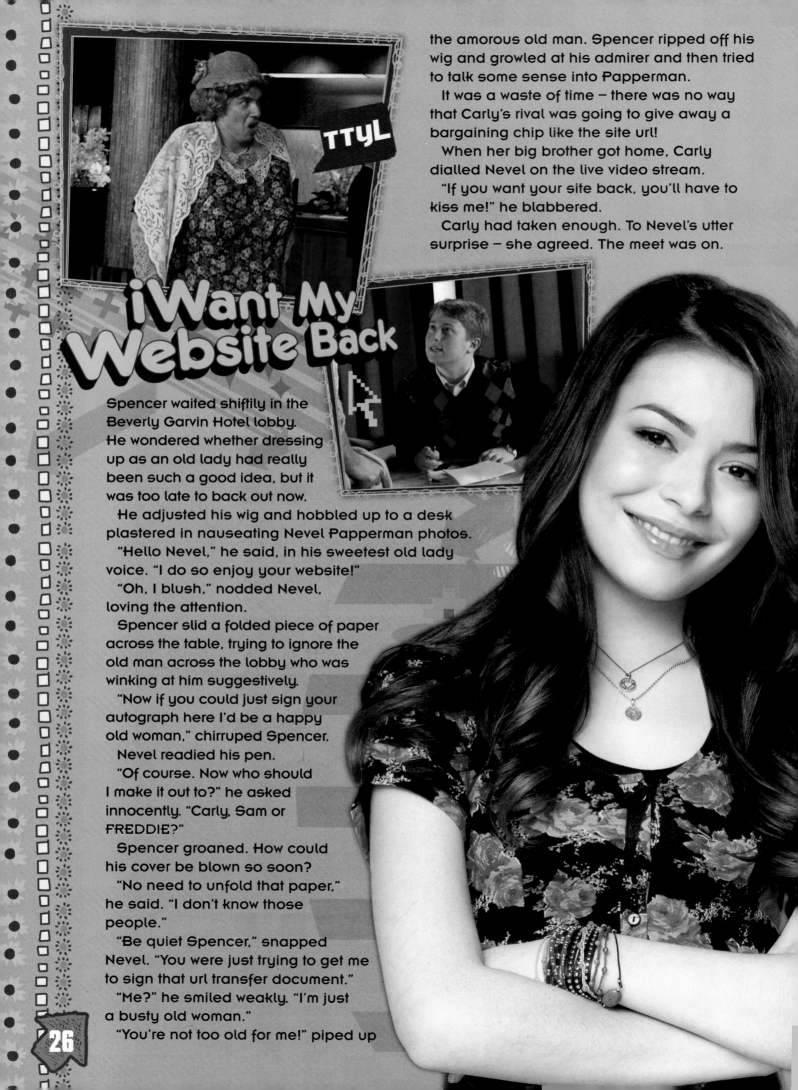

the amorous old man. Spencer ripped off his wig and growled at his admirer and then tried to talk some sense into Papperman.

It was a waste of time – there was no way that Carly's rival was going to give away a bargaining chip like the site url!

When her big brother got home, Carly dialled Nevel on the live video stream.

"If you want your site back, you'll have to kiss me!" he blabbered.

Carly had taken enough. To Nevel's utter surprise – she agreed. The meet was on.

TTyL

iWant My Website Back

Spencer waited shiftily in the Beverly Garvin Hotel lobby. He wondered whether dressing up as an old lady had really been such a good idea, but it was too late to back out now.

He adjusted his wig and hobbled up to a desk plastered in nauseating Nevel Papperman photos.

"Hello Nevel," he said, in his sweetest old lady voice. "I do so enjoy your website!"

"Oh, I blush," nodded Nevel, loving the attention.

Spencer slid a folded piece of paper across the table, trying to ignore the old man across the lobby who was winking at him suggestively.

"Now if you could just sign your autograph here I'd be a happy old woman," chirruped Spencer.

Nevel readied his pen.

"Of course. Now who should I make it out to?" he asked innocently. "Carly, Sam or FREDDIE?"

Spencer groaned. How could his cover be blown so soon?

"No need to unfold that paper," he said. "I don't know those people."

"Be quiet Spencer," snapped Nevel. "You were just trying to get me to sign that url transfer document."

"Me?" he smiled weakly. "I'm just a busty old woman."

"You're not too old for me!" piped up

Three hours' later, Carly waited in the alleyway beside her apartment, wondering if she'd done the right thing.

Suddenly Nevel stepped out of the shadows. He was looking even more loathsome then usual tonight.

"Let's just get this over with," muttered Carly.

"Nay, nay," slimed Nevel. "You will have a pleasant attitude when you kiss me or the deal's off."

"I don't trust you," replied Carly. "Sign the documents first."

Nevel nodded appreciatively. "Smart girl. Hand them over."

Carly breathed a sigh of relief, as Papperman scribbled his name on the transfer sheet. He handed the paperwork back and then clicked his

fingers. Suddenly two heavies appeared at each end of the alley.

"These are my insurance," he smirked. "To make sure that you don't try to skip out on my kiss."

"Smart boy," smiled Carly. "But first, this!"

Nevel jumped back as his

LET'S JUST GET THIS OVER WITH

rival tore open her coat to reveal an abseiling harness. In seconds, she had reached into the darkness, pulled out a cable and clicked it onto her karabiner.

"Bye Nevel!" she yelled, as she went flying up the side of Bushwell Plaza into the open window of the Shay apartment.

Papperman and his heavies were left dumbfounded on the pavement.

"Help me grab her!" shouted Freddie, hauling Carly in. "Go Spencer!"

Spencer kept reeling his fishing rod – delighted it had found a worthy use.

"I got it!" screamed Carly, flashing the transfer papers.

Sam patted her best friend on the back and then handed her a bucket of guacamole. Carly chucked it out of the window.

"You'll pay for this Carly Shay!" squealed Nevel.

The gang grinned. Now they only had to escort Mandy out the building and things would be back to normal…

27

Pillow My Head!

SPENCER HAS ORDERED SOME NEW BEDDING AT ONLINE STORE PILLOW MY HEAD, BUT HE ACCIDENTALLY TYPED IN 200 PILLOWS INSTEAD OF 2! NOW THERE ARE FEATHERS ALL OVER THE APARTMENT! FOUR OF SPENCER'S FRIENDS ARE TRYING TO HELP HIM CLEAR UP THE MESS — CAN YOU WORK OUT WHO'S WHO? WRITE THEIR NAMES IN THE BOXES.

1) Spencer Shay

2) Sam Puckett

3) Carly Shay

4)

¡WRITE MY OWN EPISODE

WHAT WOULD YOU REALLY, REALLY LOVE TO SEE HAPPEN ON ICARLY? WOULD FREDDIE FINALLY GET TOGETHER WITH HIS LONG-TERM CRUSH OR WOULD HIS LOVE/HATE RELATIONSHIP WITH SAM TAKE A ROMANTIC TURN? WOULD SPENCER WIN A PART IN THE GALAXY WARS PREQUEL? MAYBE NEVEL WOULD GET HIS ULTIMATE COMEUPPANCE OR COULD LEWBERT BE REPLACED WITH AN EVEN MEANER DOORMAN? NOW IT'S TIME TO LET YOUR PEN DO THE WALKING! USE THIS PAGE TO WRITE DOWN THE EPISODE OF YOUR DREAMS...

....

....

....

....

....

....

....

....

CARLY'S WORDSEARCH

Welcome to the strange and wonderful world of Carly Shay! Check out the webstar's list of characters, places and sayings, then see if you can locate each one in the wordsearch grid. Carly's words have been sneakily stashed – the right letters could be running forward or backwards, horizontally, vertically or diagonally.

M	A	B	M	S	V	D	R	H	E
U	S	G	I	T	R	I	S	S	K
C	S	R	V	K	A	D	E	I	O
H	I	U	B	N	S	O	C	K	O
A	R	G	O	S	U	C	L	C	B
C	A	L	P	D	A	Z	V	U	R
H	M	S	B	R	I	G	G	S	A
A	T	U	Y	H	C	H	U	R	E
L	X	M	C	S	N	I	N	F	P
A	Q	O	B	A	E	N	G	U	O
T	B	U	L	C	V	A	U	L	X
A	Q	F	F	T	E	J	N	Y	F
S	B	U	R	Y	L	L	E	B	G

Got the dozen? Now see how many words of three letters or more you can make out of the phrase

TAKE ME TO ICARLY.COM!

....

....

....

....

- ☑ **AV CLUB**
- ☑ **BELLY RUB**
- ☑ **CHIZ**
- ☑ **MARISSA**
- ☑ **MUCHACHALATAS**
- ☑ **MS BRIGGS**
- ☑ **NEVEL**
- ☑ **NUG NUG**
- ☑ **ON AIR**
- ☑ **PEARBOOK**
- ☑ **SOCKO**
- ☑ **SUCKISH**

RED VELVET CUPCAKES

Carly's a sucker for a cupcake! Red Velvet Cupcakes are her all-time faves. The sweet treats get their name from their crazy red colour and the velvety smooth texture of the cream cheese icing. Use this great recipe to make a batch, but just make sure Sam Puckett's nowhere near the kitchen when you start cooking. Sam can't be trusted with food – those cakes would be snaffled before they'd even hit the oven!

TO MAKE 24 SCRUMMY CUPCAKES, YOU WILL NEED:

- 290g of self raising flour
- 60ml red food colouring
- 2 tablespoons cocoa powder
- 115g soft unsalted butter
- 55g sugar
- 2 eggs
- 1 teaspoon vanilla essence
- 240ml buttermilk
- 1 teaspoon distilled white vinegar
- 1 teaspoon baking soda

FOR THE TOPPING:

- 250g cream cheese
- 400g icing sugar
- 150g butter
- ½ tsp vanilla essence

1. Line two 12-cup muffin trays with paper cake cases and then preheat the oven to 180°C/350°F/Gas Mark 4.

2. Sift the flour to a clean bowl and then place to one side. Mix the red food colouring and cocoa powder in another bowl, stirring until they form a smooth paste.

3. Use a wooden spoon to beat the butter and sugar together in a large mixing bowl. When the mixture is gold and creamy, crack the eggs and carefully stir them in. Add the vanilla and then pour in the red cocoa mixture.

4. Tip one third of the flour into the butter mixture, beat well, then stir in half of the buttermilk. Beat in another third of the flour and then the rest of the buttermilk. Add the last third of the flour.

5. Mix the vinegar and baking soda in a deep bowl. It will fizz, but don't worry. Tip this into the red cake mixture and stir well.

6. Fill the cake cases with the red batter and put the tins in the oven.

7. Bake the cakes for around 20 minutes. To test if the cakes are cooked, pat the tops. If the sponge springs back up, they are ready!

8. When the cupcakes are cool, stir the topping ingredients together in a small mixing bowl. Spread the creamy icing over the cakes – then eat!

KEEP YOUR KITCHEN COOL!
It's important to stay safe in the kitchen — ask an adult for permission before starting a new cooking project. Ask for help using knives or handling the oven and hob.

CROWDS OF CRAZY
CLIP IDEAS!

1. Get your groove on like Gibby! The little round one likes nothing better than dancing on tables at the Groovy Smoothie. You may not want to get jiggy around the crockery, but when your local pizzeria pipes out some music, why not stand up and get on down?

REC⦿

2. Carly might love gummy bears, but those sweet little fellas have a dark side! Stage a gummy bear battle. Pitch reds and yellows against greens and blacks. Charge!

⦿ ⊖ +

3. Next time your folks are doing something really boring like gardening, film them and create your own hilarious voiceover.

4. Put together a fruit boy band. Draw faces on your faves and get them performing their own hits. What about an exotic rendition of a Take That classic performed by Gooseberry Barlow, Raspberry Williams and Jason Orange?

⦿ ⊖ +

5. Wait until it rains hard, pop on your swimsuit, then take a shower outdoors. Don't forget to lather up with your gel and shampoo.

REC⦿

6. Dress up your dog like your dad. How does he look in the old man's best hat, scarf and reading glasses?

⦿ ⊖ +

7. Channel the Karate Kid and then attempt to catch a fly with a pair of chopsticks.

8. FIND OUT WHAT YOU'D LOOK LIKE IF YOU HAD COOKED SPAGHETTI FOR HAIR.

Have you dreamt about recording your own clip for iCarly.com? There's no guarantee that the crew will feature any tape sent in, but if the clip is daft, nutty or downright immature enough, it stands a good chance of getting on! Find yourself a camcorder and then rope some friends into starring in a silly skit or a comedy dance routine. If you need a little extra inspiration, check out this wicked list! These pages are packed with 50 fab ideas. Each one is sure to lead you to comedy gold, just make sure you don't forget to press the record button.

9. Hold an earwig marathon – try placing them on a map of central London, then see if they can make it from Greenwich to the Mall via Canary Wharf.

10. EaT SOME SOUP WITH a FORK.

11. Write 'forgotten something, Mum?' on every page of an entire pad of sticky post-it notes. Now cover yourself in them from head to toe.

12. Stage your own episode of 'Bangkok Sings', the Thai version of a reality singing show, then belt out a version of David Archuleta's hits in a high-pitched voice.

13. Try to beat the world record for ripping up a phone book. If you need help, involve as many mates as you need to tear that tome in two.

14. Make and perform a crazy poem replacing every letter of the alphabet with random words, from avocado to zebra.

15. Did you know that experts say you should floss between your toes three times a day? The iCarly gang are fascinated by this! Film your family practising good foot health.

16. We all love an awkward photo, so pose with an unsuspecting member of your family. Maybe it's time to wheel out your old Aunt Mabel with no teeth and the beginnings of a beard.

17. Whipping your hair back and forth is like, so last year. Gibby loves whirling his vest in the air – can you make like the Gibster?

18. What would you look like as a tiger? Would you be as cute as a real hamster? Use computer wizardry to mutate your own face onto a host of furry friends.

19. HaVe a WeLLie-THROWING CONTEST WITH YOUR PaLS.

20. Carly loves the Build-A-Bra store. Can you customise your own bra with tassels or bling and show it off on the outside of your clothes? If you don't own one (or you're a boy!), borrow your mum's or big sister's. Just make sure you ask first.

21. It's always good to see things from another's perspective. Why not make your own version of Lewbert's wart and wear it for the day? Film other people's reactions so that you can empathise with the warty one.

22. Build your own version of the Proton Cruiser and film yourself in it. Don't forget to make Spencer-like sound effects as you fire the laser guns. Pyoo, pyoo, pyoo...

23. See if you or your friends can perform a silly walk for the cameras!

24. Try superimposing your face onto a noted monument or piece of art. Will you be the Mona Lisa or part of Mt Rushmore?

25. It's dangerous, but effective – can you juggle toilet brushes without accidentally grabbing the gross end?

26. Spin round in a wheelie chair and then try walking in a straight line.

27. PUT ON a BIZARRE VEGETABLE PARADE.

28. See what you'd look like if your eyebrows were higher. Draw them with an eyeliner pen half way up your forehead. Now blank your own real ones out with sticky tape or skin-coloured make-up.

29. Do some random river dancing. You'll need to keep your torso very still, hands by your sides, while moving your legs very fast.

30. Double Trouble. Find your own lookie-likey in the park or around town and then capture yourselves on film.

31. Hold a chicken-eating contest, but make sure you do it in the style of Henry VIII. This means no knives, forks or serviettes allowed! As Sam would say, 'Mama loves da chicken'.

32. Do a headstand while playing the recorder, flute or even the violin. Respect!

33. Fold your body into a weird position. Can you lick your own toes or use your arms as a skipping rope? Eurgh and Ouch!

34. Moustachorama! Make some fake moustaches using felt, the bristles of a brush or even by holding your own ponytail or the end of the dog's tail across your upper lip. Are you a Sherlock Holmes or a Charlie Chaplin?

35. If you can't have a bath in baked beans, why not wash your face in tomato soup?

36. Write and perform your own Pointless Play – how about one featuring four babies fighting over a bottle of milk? It'll end in tears!

37. Be your own worst enemy – release your inner Nevel and film yourself arguing with your reflection in the mirror.

38. Spencer once made a Labradoodle artwork for a client's wife. Create your own mixed breed dog sculpture and present it live on air. How about a cockapoo (a cocker spaniel/poodle cross) or a Bogle (beagle/boxer combination)?

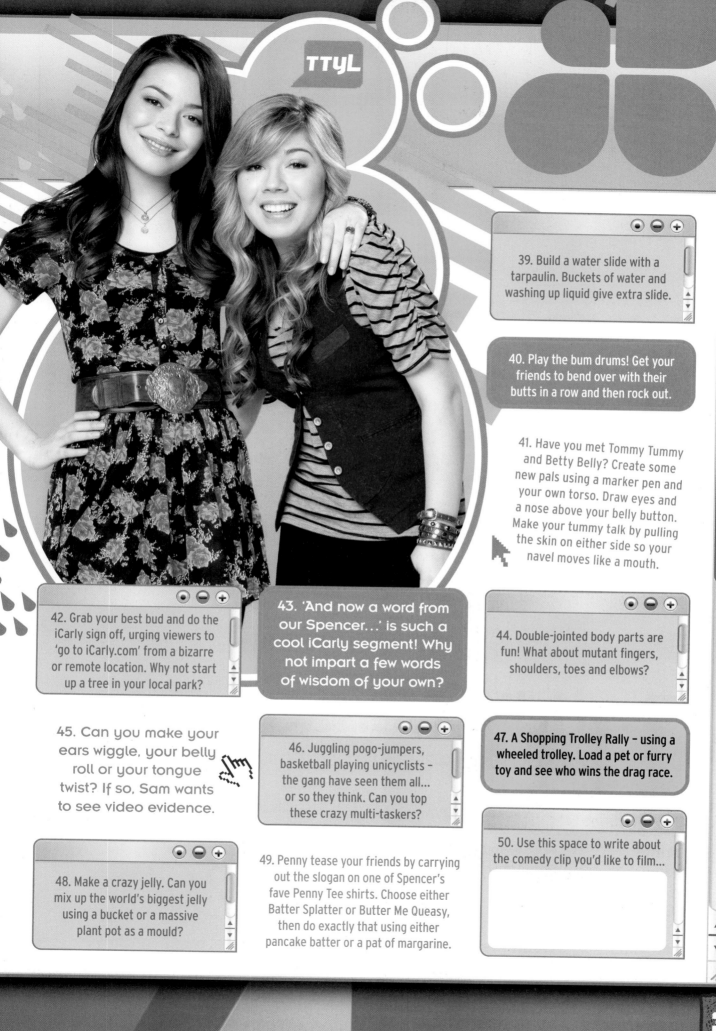

TTyL

39. Build a water slide with a tarpaulin. Buckets of water and washing up liquid give extra slide.

40. Play the bum drums! Get your friends to bend over with their butts in a row and then rock out.

41. Have you met Tommy Tummy and Betty Belly? Create some new pals using a marker pen and your own torso. Draw eyes and a nose above your belly button. Make your tummy talk by pulling the skin on either side so your navel moves like a mouth.

42. Grab your best bud and do the iCarly sign off, urging viewers to 'go to iCarly.com' from a bizarre or remote location. Why not start up a tree in your local park?

43. 'And now a word from our Spencer…' is such a cool iCarly segment! Why not impart a few words of wisdom of your own?

44. Double-jointed body parts are fun! What about mutant fingers, shoulders, toes and elbows?

45. Can you make your ears wiggle, your belly roll or your tongue twist? If so, Sam wants to see video evidence.

46. Juggling pogo-jumpers, basketball playing unicyclists – the gang have seen them all… or so they think. Can you top these crazy multi-taskers?

47. A Shopping Trolley Rally – using a wheeled trolley. Load a pet or furry toy and see who wins the drag race.

48. Make a crazy jelly. Can you mix up the world's biggest jelly using a bucket or a massive plant pot as a mould?

49. Penny tease your friends by carrying out the slogan on one of Spencer's fave Penny Tee shirts. Choose either Batter Splatter or Butter Me Queasy, then do exactly that using either pancake batter or a pat of margarine.

50. Use this space to write about the comedy clip you'd like to film…

Freddie Benson

 Profile ▼

is installing great new software on my Pearbook

▼ Personal Info:

Full name:	Fredward Benson
Birthday:	February 14th
Star Sign:	Aquarius
Hair Colour:	Brown
Eye Colour:	Brown
Freddie likes: 👍	Wearing my Nub Nub Galaxy Wars costume, hugging Carly
Freddie dislikes: 👎	Being picked up, pranked or punched by Sam

FOR REAL!

Freddie has 899 SplashFace Supporters, scroll down to view more

899 friends

See All

Gibby Gibson

Spencer Shay

Carly Shay

Sam Puckett

Surprising SplashFace Fact: x

I'm prone to random outbursts in Spanish.

Latest Wall Posts

Sam:
Can you help me with my maths homework, I don't have the text book?

Freddie:
Where is it?

Sam:
I sold it.

Freddie:
Then, no!

Carly:
Come on you guys, you know I hate it when you fight.

Freddie:
She started it.

Sam:
Did not!

Freddie:
Did so!

Carly is now offline.

Draw or stick in your own profile picture **and write your** name and comment.

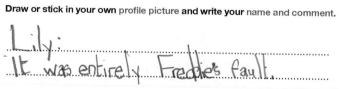

Lily:
It was entirely Freddie's fault.

Start 2 Finish

As an iCarly fan you'll know that every episode of your favourite show is a roller coaster ride, packed full of plot twists and turns and even the occasional loop-the-loop! These pages are packed with some of the funniest storylines, but to relive the action you'll have to untangle them first. Read through the list of episode beginnings below and then study the jumbled episode endings on the opposite page. Now draw lines to match up the two halves. Can you end each episode correctly? If you get stuck, the answers are on page 77.

STARTS

1. There's trouble for iCarly.com when Carly's doorman is injured after a confetti cannon in a faux muffin basket explodes whilst filming a segment of 'Messin' with Lewbert'.

2. Carly, Sam and Freddie film the rotting of a peanut butter and jelly sandwich...

3. Sam and Carly meet a boy called Jeffrey who says that his father has suggested running a cool new contest.

4. When a letter addressed to apartment 13B is accidentally delivered to Carly and Spencer, Lewbert reveals that the property has been deserted for years.

5. An iCarly webcast draws attention from the Seattle Police Department when a store clerk suspected of making pirated DVDs is spotted walking behind 'Crazy Fruit Dude' on the show segment 'Who's That Weirdo in My Neighborhood?'.

6. The iCarly gang is delighted to be invited to film backstage at a mixed martial arts centre.

7. In a romance-packed episode, Carly and Freddie hook Sam up with Freddie's friend Jonah.

8. Spencer is over the moon to receive his new credit card, but panic ensues when Carly finds he's cancelled his old one.

ENDINGS

A. Nevel demands a kiss from Carly as payment for transferring the rights to iCarly.com back to their rightful owner. Luckily Carly escapes with her website intact.

B. Carly, Sam and Freddie are treated to the première of Spencer's claymation movie, 'The Alien, the Space Hamster and the Burrito'.

C. Spencer handcuffs a bully he once knew at summer camp to the couch and then spanks him in front of his young son.

D. Freddie's mum Marissa blames Lewbert after he shows no sympathy when her son mysteriously falls down the stairs.

E. Spencer, bruised and furious, grounds Carly for at least two weeks.

F. Spencer finds himself mobbed by angry children.

G. Freddie proves that he was not trying to steal Gibby's girlfriend Tasha away, prompting Gibby to apologise to everyone.

H. The gang manage to stop iCarly being shut down for fraud.

For extra bragging points, can you also identify the episodes featured above? Write in the correct number and letter next to each one.

7		iHate Sam's Boyfriend
		iGive Away a Car
6	E	iLook Alike
		iStakeout

4		iScream on Halloween
1	0	iHurt Lewbert
		iWant My Website Back
	G	iEnrageGibby

iMust Have Locker #239

Locker #239 had been the best locker at Ridgeway High for years, but how much would Carly, Sam and Freddie do to get their hands on it?

Carly and her friends were wrapping up the latest webisode of iCarly, with a cool new art feature. Some wacko called Chad had been sending 2,000 emails a week, asking the guys to draw bunnies and display them on the show.

Sam and Freddie lifted up flip charts, revealing their rabbity works of art.

"I hope you enjoyed my bunny, Chad!" goofed Fred.

Sam hit the applause button and Carly unveiled her creation.

Freddie didn't want to laugh, but he couldn't help it. Carly's drawing was totally lame!

"Hey," groaned Carly. "Quit laughing!"

"It's pretty bad, kid!" giggled Sam, wondering why the animal looked more like a kindergarten's work than that of an international web sensation.

Carly tried not to blush as she wrapped up the show – being bad at drawing was pretty embarrassing, especially when your big brother was a professional artist.

"Maybe your bunny had a terrible accident?" teased Sam, pointing at its weird mutated ears.

Carly couldn't resist a smile. "It's a lot better than the first bunny I drew."

Sam and Freddie both gasped as their pal turned to the next page of her flip chart.

"Why's your bunny wearing fuzzy slippers?" asked Freddie.

Carly frowned. "Those are his feet."

Sam pointed at the pair of bullet holes in the poor creature's head and Carly explained that they were eyes.

"OK," said Freddie. "But why is he carrying a hose?"

"Duh!" snapped Carly. "Because he's got a part-time job as a volunteer firefighter!"

Freddie flashed a look at Sam.

Of course.

At school the next day, Gibby was strolling through the hall topless when Mr Howard started running after him like a demented squirrel.

"Hey, you there!" he thundered. "You know the rules. You're required to wear a shirt during school hours."

Gibby pulled out a copy of the school handbook. He had no desire to upset authority, but when it came to being shirtless – he knew his rights.

"Check the handbook, Mr Howard," he suggested helpfully. "Page seventy-four."

Howard snatched the book and scanned through. No boob tubes, no vests, turtlenecks…

"Does it say I've got to wear a shirt?" pressed Gibby.

The teacher's defeated expression said it all. "Carry on."

Point made, Gibby wandered over to say hi to

WHAT'S THE BIG DEAL?

Freddie and Carly. He was just asking for some stomach lotion when Sam slammed into the lockers.

"Richard Weitz is moving to Switzerland!"

Carly paled. Richard Weitz was the lucky tenant of Locker #239. If he was in Europe, the locker would have to be available! It had to be the first time ever in the middle of the school year!

"What's the big deal?" asked Gibby.

"It's the best locker in the whole school," sighed Carly.

"When they were building Ridgeway, some worker screwed up and ordered a locker that's four times the size of a regular locker," explained Freddie.

"Plus it's next to a big window," added Sam.

Freddie got a far away look in his eye. "The cheerleaders walk past it on their way to practise."

Gibby started to appreciate the deal about #239. It really was a locker with a view.

"Principal Franklin is going to hold a contest to find out who gets it next," added Sam.

That was one contest that she intended to win.

That night, Carly had two important things on her mind – winning locker #239 and sorting out her dubious bunny-drawing skills. It was time for a sister-to-brother chat.

"How would you feel about giving me art lessons Spencer?" asked Carly.

His little sister nodded. At last someone who could interpret her work!

At school, Principal Franklin wasted no time in launching his locker competition. He flipped on a microphone and then summoned the students' attention.

SO HE'S a Part-time fireman?

Spencer looked delighted. "I would love to! When did you get interested in art?"

Carly shrugged and then reluctantly showed him her bunny sketch. There was a long silence.

"Well, say something!" she pleaded.

"I don't think I should," gulped Spencer. "At least you're capable of holding a pencil. You've got the potential to be a great artist."

Carly felt so relieved, she decided to show her brother her first attempt at a bunny sketch.

This time Spencer squinted and stood back so he could get a better look.

"So he's a part-time fireman?"

"Only one of you will be lucky enough to win #239," he announced, pointing to the sacred locker.

Carly, Freddie and Sam's classmates oohed in wonder.

The Principal pointed to a large glass case that had been filled to the brim with Fat Cakes. The student who could guess the number of cakes in the tank was going to win the locker.

Kids started frantically sharing their guessing strategies. Freddie's was based on linear algebra. Sam was based on instinct.

"Mama knows her Fat Cakes," she whispered, scribbling down her answer.

iMUSt Have Locker #239

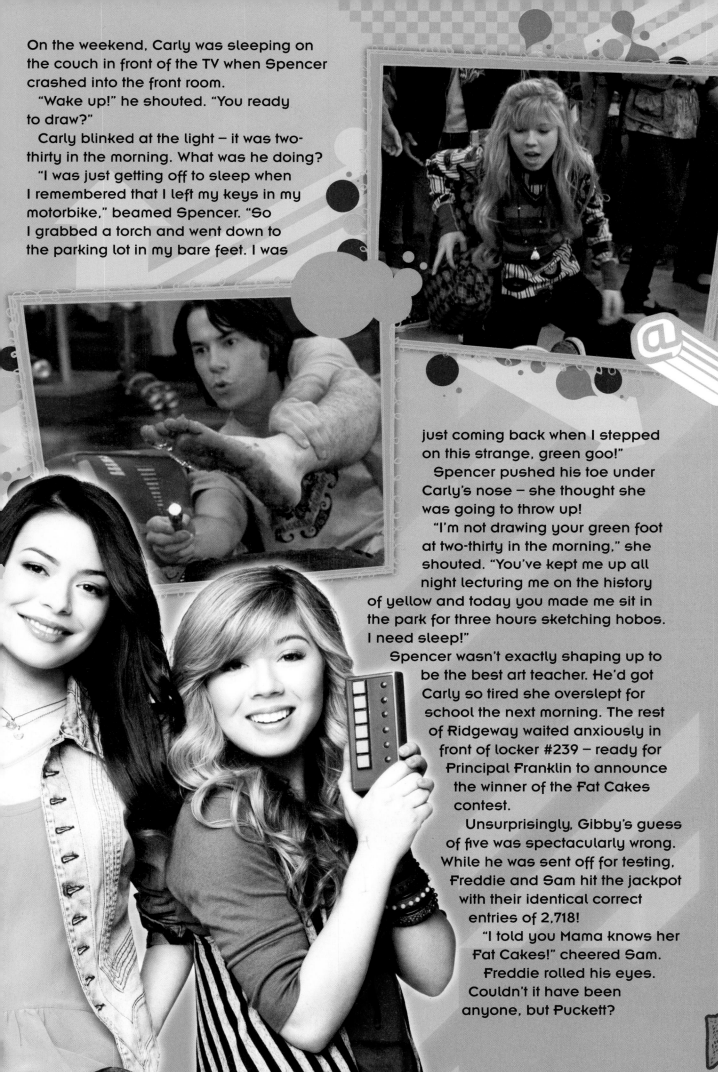

On the weekend, Carly was sleeping on the couch in front of the TV when Spencer crashed into the front room.

"Wake up!" he shouted. "You ready to draw?"

Carly blinked at the light – it was two-thirty in the morning. What was he doing?

"I was just getting off to sleep when I remembered that I left my keys in my motorbike," beamed Spencer. "So I grabbed a torch and went down to the parking lot in my bare feet. I was just coming back when I stepped on this strange, green goo!"

Spencer pushed his toe under Carly's nose – she thought she was going to throw up!

"I'm not drawing your green foot at two-thirty in the morning," she shouted. "You've kept me up all night lecturing me on the history of yellow and today you made me sit in the park for three hours sketching hobos. I need sleep!"

Spencer wasn't exactly shaping up to be the best art teacher. He'd got Carly so tired she overslept for school the next morning. The rest of Ridgeway waited anxiously in front of locker #239 – ready for Principal Franklin to announce the winner of the Fat Cakes contest.

Unsurprisingly, Gibby's guess of five was spectacularly wrong. While he was sent off for testing, Freddie and Sam hit the jackpot with their identical correct entries of 2,718!

"I told you Mama knows her Fat Cakes!" cheered Sam.

Freddie rolled his eyes. Couldn't it have been anyone, but Puckett?

iMUSt Have LOCKer #239

Art lessons with Spencer got worse. This afternoon, Carly was helping him build a sculpture out of spatulas.

"No-no," winced Spencer. "You need to put that spatula next to the other one over there."

"What does this have to do with drawing?" gasped Carly.

Spencer took a deep breath. "If you learn to work with three-dimensional art it makes two-dimensional art much easier. Now tighten up that ballpeen bracket."

Carly gave up. She didn't even know what a ballpeen bracket was! Instead of tightening the sculpture, she decided to quit Spencer's art lessons.

"I get it!" shouted Spencer. "You think I'm a terrible person."

His little sister kicked the couch. "I didn't say that."

With an angry clatter, the spatula sculpture collapsed.

Spencer stalked off to his room, muttering about the importance of ballpeen brackets.

A few days later, things were still tense in the Shay apartment. Carly tried to creep out with a sketchpad under her arm while Spencer let off some tension by making a new mud sculpture.

"Why do you have a pad?" demanded Spencer, grabbing it with a muddy hand.

Carly confessed. "I'm taking an art class at the community centre."

"You got yourself another art teacher!?" bawled Spencer.

"Don't get all hurt," sighed Carly. "I just wanted to draw a bunny."

Spencer scowled and then flipped open the pad. He grabbed a pencil and sketched an amazing rabbit at lightning speed.

"I'm sorry," said Carly. "That is a top notch bunny."

Freddie expected his new locker to be fun, but he didn't count on a total party to be raging in front of it. When he turned up with his key, Sam and a dozen of her rowdiest mates had transformed #239 into an in-house entertainment centre!

"What is going on here?" Freddie demanded, checking the kids with glowsticks rocking out to the plasma TV fitted on the locker door.

Sam jumped in the air, pulling off a great electric guitar lick. Somehow she'd even managed to connect up a state-of-the-art gaming system!

"What? It's my locker," she pouted.

Freddie begged to disagree. "Make that our locker."

SINCE WHEN DID YOU TURN INTO MY WIFE?

Sam elbowed Benson out of the way.

"Since when did you turn into my wife?" she argued, reaching for the remote. "Check out what I did."

Sam clicked a button and disco lights started to flash from the locker. The music turned up 20 notches and everyone began random dancing.

"You're going to get us in big trouble," argued Freddie.

"I just made it into a little hang-out," replied Sam.

Suddenly a kid from Sam's detention class scooted round the corner.

"Teacher!"

Sam slammed the remote into Freddie's hand, skidding down the corridor just as Mr Howard stormed up in the other direction.

"Oh great," hissed Freddie, trying to turn off the music and laser beams.

Mr Howard had seen too much already.

"Come with me," he barked, dragging Benson by the collar.

"Awww…"

TTYL

45

splattered brother back to the apartment. His outburst had got the pair of them banned from the college for life!

"I'm a big jerk," admitted Spencer. "And now I've got paint up my nose."

Carly was about to give him a hug, when Ms Fielder knocked at the front door.

"I followed the paint trail," she gushed. "They don't teach you to be spontaneous in art school. Maybe you could teach me?"

Spencer reached over and gave her a passionate, painty kiss.

"OK," said Carly. "So I don't understand art."

iMUST Have LOCKER #239

Over at the Community Centre, Carly was loving her art class. Her teacher, Ms Fielder, was so sweet and she'd already made great progress.

"Today people we're going to continue our work with straight lines," smiled Ms Fielder. "Instead of coloured pencils we're going to using paint."

Knock! Knock! Carly's face crumpled in horror as Spencer popped his head round the door!

"I just came here to see what a good art teacher is like," he smiled sarcastically. "I was wondering if I could observe your 'class' tonight."

Ms Fielder nodded and then got everyone started on their straight lines.

It was too much for Spencer. "How does painting straight lines help people learn art?" he asked.

"It teaches patience and control," replied Ms Fielder, raising her voice. "Something you seem to be lacking."

Carly wanted to self-combust.

"What about being creative, spontaneous and passionate?" yelled Spencer.

Ms Fielder was even madder. She took a paintbrush and daubed Spencer with blue paint. Spencer grabbed a paintbrush and replied in the only way he knew how.

"OK," nodded Carly. "This is going to get worse before it gets better…"

An hour later, Carly took her paint-

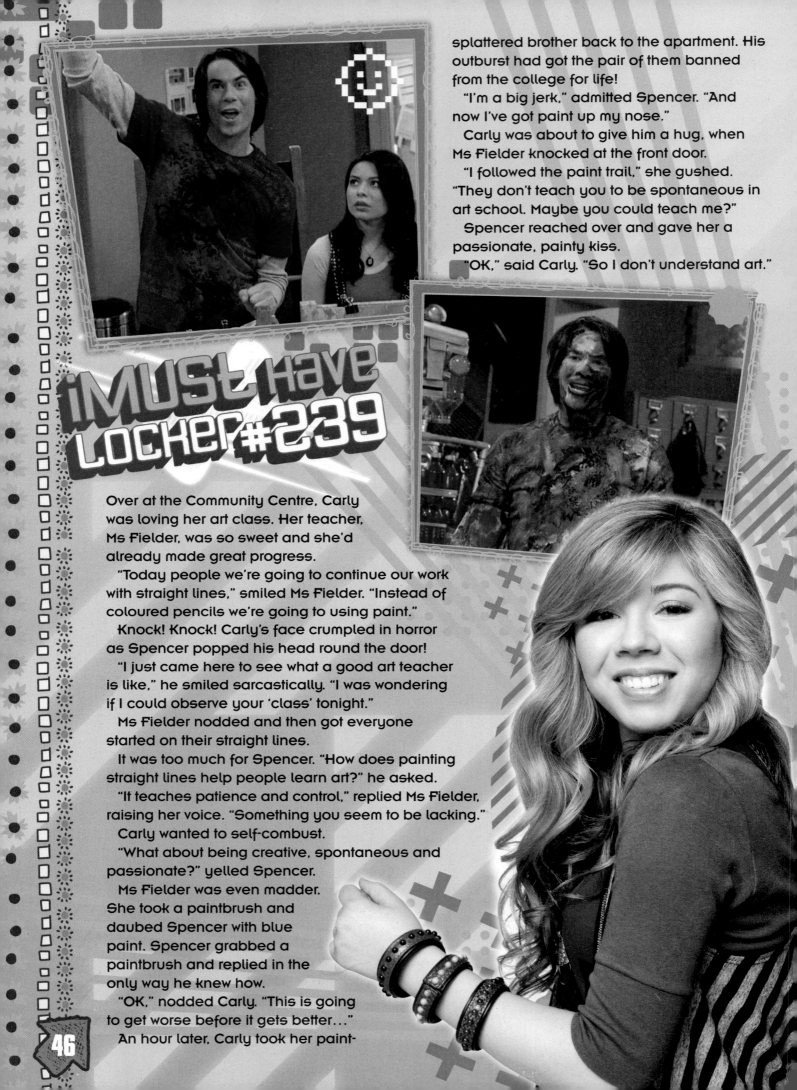

After maths, Freddie sprinted to get to the locker before Sam did. He dialled the combination again and again, but #239 wasn't opening.

"Oh, butter!" swore Freddie. What was she up to now?

Just then, Puckett strolled down the hall as cool as a cucumber. She explained casually how she'd changed the combination just to irritate the techy tech producer.

"That's it!" grimaced Fred. "I can't share a locker with you anymore."

"No time to talk now dude," shrugged Sam. "My mum just had laser eye surgery and she's waiting outside to pick me up."

The thought of Sam's mum driving a car at any time made Freddie shiver, but after eye surgery!

"Listen," he insisted. "I'm prepared to offer you 200 bucks for your half of the locker."

Sam was impressed. "Done."

"Really?" gasped Freddie. "I thought you'd ask for more."

Sam shook her head. "I've been missing having a locker next to Carly so I was going to give you that one anyway."

Freddie kicked the wall – she'd got him yet again! He already knew there was no point asking for his money back.

CRASH!!

Sam and Freddie leapt out of the way as Mrs Puckett's station wagon reversed straight through the hall window, destroying locker #239 in one devastating blow.

"Nice driving, Mum!" roared Sam, climbing in the boot.

There was a skid of tyres and the beat-up car screeched away.

"Goodbye locker #239," sighed Freddie. "And my money."

Inevitably, Mr Howard chose that moment to walk round the corner. Freddie felt his collar being grasped, dragging him away from the wreckage of the locker he would never have again.

"Come with me!"

TOO COOL FOR SCHOOL?

Pick the descriptions below that sound most like you. Circle your answers and tot up how many of each letter you get. Check the panel on the right to find out how you deal with school life!

1. IT'S THE ELECTIONS FOR SCHOOL COUNCIL. DO YOU...

A Put your hand up straight away and hope that someone seconds you.

B Wait and see if anyone puts you forward – you have other stuff going on and aren't sure you'll have time to commit to an extra activity.

C Vote for your friends. You're not going to put your name in the ring.

2. AT LUNCHTIME YOU...

A Eat lunch and then head off to a club.

B Enjoy lunch and make the most of the break from classes. Your brain is fried!

C Wait until the last sitting – the dinner ladies always give second helpings out at the end of lunchtime.

3. IN THE PLAYGROUND YOU SPOT SOMEONE BEING BULLIED. DO YOU...

A Feel sorry for them, but thank your lucky stars it isn't you.

B Call a teacher. You hate bullies.

C Wade in and give the bully a taste of their own medicine.

4. THE SUBJECT YOU ENJOY MOST IS...

A IT

B Home Economics

C PE

5. YOU MOST DISLIKE TEACHERS WHO...

A Tell you off for bringing in a mobile phone or video games.

B Are uncool and fuddy duddy.

C Can't see that there's more to life than tests.

6. IN CLASS YOU ARE MOST LIKELY TO GET TOLD OFF FOR...

A Not paying attention.

B Chatting.

C Forgetting your homework.

7. YOUR ANNUAL SCHOOL REPORT USUALLY READS...

A Likeable, sociable, with an enquiring mind.

B Attentive, gifted and conscientious.

C Sharp and able, but needs to work harder to their achieve potential.

8. AT THE SCHOOL PROM, YOU'RE MOST LIKELY TO COME...

A In a ballgown or tux – you like to look good.

B In fancy dress – you love to have fun.

C In jeans – you're not into all that dressing-up nonsense.

9. YOUR SCHOOL YEARBOOK WOULD READ 'CLASSMATE MOST LIKELY TO...'

A 'Work with Steven Spielberg'.

B 'Win the Nobel Peace Prize'.

C 'Make a million'.

10. YOU'LL PROBABLY REMEMBER YOUR SCHOOL DAYS AS...

A The best days of your life.

B A necessary part of growing up.

C Fun, in parts.

When it comes to school, every kid has got a different survival technique. How do you cope with pottery, playgrounds and popularity tests? Are you more 'teacher's pest' than 'teacher's pet'? Find out if you're too cool for school!

★ MOSTLY AS

Like Freddie you really enjoy school and are an enthusiastic student, although you excel in some subjects more than others. You really enjoy the social aspect of class and take part in lots of extra-curricular activities too. Just make sure that you don't sign up for too many clubs – everyone needs to chillax sometimes!

★ MOSTLY BS

You're an A-Grade student, just like Carly Shay. You enjoy school and love learning, but you also like to have fun. This sometimes gets you into trouble and means that although you hand your homework in and are consistently top of the class, you manage to avoid being seen as the school swot.

★ MOSTLY CS

OK so school isn't always Sam Puckett's preferred place to be, but that doesn't mean she can't and won't learn. Like her, you have a quick mind and there are certain subjects that capture your imagination. Your strong character means you're not the kind of kid to be bullied and you're brave enough to forge your own path rather than following the crowd.

STARRING YOU!

I ♥ Make Sam Girlier

CAST

WRITE THE ACTORS' NAMES IN HERE!

★ **CARLY SHAY**

Played by:
Eva Schralltuts

★ **SAM PUCKETT**

Played by:
Lily Topham

★ **JOCELYN**

Played by:
_____

★ **EVAN**

Played by:
_____

★ **WENDY**

Played by:
_____

★ **MR STERN**

Played by:
_____

Think you and your crew would make great new cast members on the iCarly show? Use this script to give yourselves an impromptu audition! As well as featuring lots of lines for the starring roles, this scene also has lots of interesting extras to test your character acting to the limit. Who's got what it takes to play the new school bully Jocelyn or the bespectacled teacher, Mr Stern?

Decide who will play the parts and then get everyone together for a read-through. The lines are the actual ones used in a real iCarly episode where Sam tries to revamp her image so a cute boy will like her. Once everyone has got a feel for the scene, learn the words and try acting it out as naturally as possible. When you think you're ready to perform the scene, make sure someone's on hand to get it on camera!

Episode 216: iMake Sam Girlier
Act1, ScE Interior, schoolHallway, day.

Sam is at her locker. There's a big swing bin next to her. Sam pulls a carton of eggs out of her locker and drops it in the bin. Carly approaches and noticing what Sam is doing, stops and waits for a bit. Sam pulls some cans of spray paint and drops them in the bin, too. Next comes a box labelled 'KABOOM'. After a deep sigh, Sam drops that in the rubbish. Carly approaches Sam.

CARLY: Why are you cleaning out your locker?

SAM: Just am.

Carly reaches into the bin and pulls out the carton of eggs.

CARLY: But these are your throwing eggs.

SAM: Sighs I know.

CARLY: OK, why've you been acting all weird since the party?

SAM: It's no big deal, just forget about it…

We hear a boy scream off-screen. Carly, Sam and some other kids cross over to see a tough older girl named Jocelyn holding a twelve-year-old boy called Evan upside down by his ankles.

JOCELYN: Next time I sneeze, you better say God bless you!

EVAN: I will! I'm sorry!

Carly sees Wendy standing nearby.

CARLY: To Wendy Who is that girl?

WENDY: Some chick named Jocelyn.

CARLY: And she's a student?

WENDY: Uh-huh. She's a senior.

Episode 216: iMake Sam Girlier

CARLY: Yeah, a senior citizen.

EVAN: **Still dangling** Lemme down!

JOCELYN: No!

EVAN: Could someone call the police?

CARLY: **To Sam** Maybe you should stop her.

SAM: Why me?

CARLY: Y'know, 'cos you're...

SAM: Just 'cos some bully's pickin' on a kid doesn't mean I have to go in there and...

Mr Stern enters the scene. He walks fast to Jocelyn.

MR STERN: **Loud** Hey! Hey, break it up! Put that boy down right now!

Jocelyn drops Evan. He screams and runs off.

JOCELYN: You irritate me!

Jocelyn walks off. The bell rings.

MR STERN: **Loud** C'mon, you people are gonna be late for homeroom. Go. Go on.

Mr Stern shoos all the kids out of the hall. Carly and Sam are the last two remaining.

SAM: **Shuts her locker** We better go.

Carly grabs Sam's arm and turns her back around.

CARLY: No.

SAM: We're gonna be late.

CARLY: I don't care, what's bothering you?

Sam looks around to check no one is looking.

SAM: OK. When everyone was making their speeches about me at the party, it made me feel... icky.

CARLY: Why? They said nice stuff.

SAM: Yeah. Pete said he'd want me for backup if he ever got in a fight, and then he called me a 'duuude'.

CARLY: **Chuckles** So?

Episode 216: iMake Sam Girlier

SAM: So, unless I reeeaaaally got this whole biology thing mixed up, I am not a dude.

CARLY: Oh, that's just an expression. People call me dude. Sometimes.

SAM: It's different. When people think of you they don't think of fighting and pranks and vicious behaviour.

CARLY: But that's who you are. You're lovable and vicious. Like your rabid cat Frothy.

SAM: I want guys like Pete to think of me as just lovable... not the person to call when there's a riot, or they wanna tip a truck over.

CARLY: So, you wanna like, change your image?

SAM: **Beat and embarrassed** Would you help me?

CARLY: 'Course. But what do you want me to...

SAM: I wanna be more like you. Y'know, all soft and girly and weak.

CARLY: Well... then you're gonna have to really commit. No more fighting...

SAM: Done.

CARLY: No more pranks, no more spitting for distance...

SAM: That's all over.

CARLY: And you can't wear boxer shorts to school anymore.

SAM: Why?!

CARLY: If you wanna be soft and girly, you gotta switch to...

SAM: Don't say it!

CARLY: I was just gonna say...

SAM: Don't!

CARLY: OK! I won't say it.

SAM: Thanks.

CARLY: **In a small voice** Panties.

SAM: Ahhhhhh!!!

Sam hurries off. Carly chuckles, following after her.

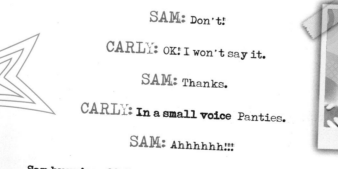

Spencer Shay

 Profile ▼

is trying to break my Pak-Rat video gaming record

▼ Personal Info:

Full name:	Spencer Shay
Birthday:	November 11th
Star Sign:	Scorpio
Hair Colour:	Brown
Eye Colour:	Brown
Spencer likes: 👍	Sculpting, Socko and Mr Galini's Coconut Cream Pie
Spencer dislikes: 👎	My magic meatball, mean Chuck Chambers who lives down the hall

WEB PAGE!

Spencer has 420 SplashFace Supporters, scroll down to view more

420 friends   See All

Freddie Benson

Sam Puckett

Gibby Gibson

Carly Shay

Surprising SplashFace Fact: x

I love to drink milk in the shower!

Latest Wall Posts

Freddie:
Want a fencing rematch on Saturday? Also, there's a new director's cut of Galaxy Wars showing if you feel like catching a movie afterwards.

Spencer:
No to the fencing, but 'pyoo', 'pyoo', 'pyoo', absolutely yes to the awesome GW movie bonanza!

Freddie:
Great, see you at 6.

Lewbert:
Tell Carly and Sam to stop singing in my lobby. I HATE singing. Tell them I have more falafels and I'm not afraid to use/lose them.

Carly:
He's insane! You're insane Lewbert!

Draw or stick in your own profile picture **and write your** name and comment.

....
....
....
....
....

TOTALLY CONNECTED!

Carly, Sam and Freddie are always online and up for a chat! The guys spend their days virtual poking each other, instant messaging and pinging silly photos between each other via the World Wide Web.

WHAT ABOUT YOU? ARE YOU A COOL, CONNECTED CUSTOMER TOO? USE THIS PAGE TO TELL THE GANG ABOUT YOUR FAVOURITE GADGETS, SITES AND PHONE FUN.

Apart from iCarly.com, the site I click on 24/7 is

The blogging name that I have (or would like to give myself) is

The best links in the world are to

1 ....
2 ....
3 ....

The most hilarious email joke I read was about

The artist with the most downloads on my MP3 is

The funniest picture I ever snapped on my phone was

The most random instant message chat I had was with

The next bit of cool kit I'd like to save up for is

HOT TO SPOT!

CARLY AND HER BUDDIES HAVE BEEN ASKED TO POSE IN A MAGAZINE PHOTOSHOOT FOR THE IWEB AWARDS! THE CREW ARE TOTALLY PSYCHED BECAUSE THE FEATURE WILL BRING MAXIMUM EXPOSURE TO THE SITE. TAKE A PEEK AT THE SHOTS THAT THE MAGAZINE EDITOR IS CONSIDERING. PHOTO A LOOKS AWESOME, BUT SOMETHING HAS GONE SERIOUSLY WRONG IN PHOTO B. USE A PEN TO CIRCLE THE SIX DIFFERENCES.

GIBBY Up Close

Gibby

👤 Profile ▼

is wearing a stupid hat, because Sam made me! edit

▼ Personal Info:

Full name:	Charles Gibson
Birthday:	January 20th
Star Sign:	Capricorn
Hair Colour:	Brown
Eye Colour:	Brown
Gibby likes: 👍	My dog, Mr Nubbles, eating stuff on a stick at the Groovy Smoothie
Gibby dislikes: 👎	Anyone who gives me trouser wedgies, balloons

And Personal! <3

Gibby has 6,017 SplashFace Supporters, scroll down to view more:

6,017 friends   See All

Freddie Benson

Carly Shay

Sam Puckett

Spencer Shay

Latest Wall Posts

Carly:
FYI the Cheesecake Warehouse are doing an all you can eat for 5 dollars offer on Tuesdays.

Gibby:
Thanks, I'll go and check it out.

Carly:
I'm not sure they've thought it through. How much cheesecake do you think you can eat in one day, Gibby?

Sam:
Got your message about the party you're planning. Very excited about the punching booth where guests walk in and get whacked – more than happy to do the honours. Text me the details…

Draw or stick in your own profile picture **and write your** name and comment.

....
....
....
....
....

Suprising SplashFace Fact: x

I have front row seats at LA Lakers basketball games, but I let David Beckham use them occasionally.

Putting Words IN THEIR MOUTHS

1. SAM
2. GIBBY
3. PRINCIPAL FRANKLIN
4. SPENCER
5. NEVEL PAPPERMAN
6. FREDDIE
7. CARLY
8. MRS BENSON

Don't people say the goofiest things? Read through these knockout lines from the show and then match the speaker with the correct quote. Can you score an awesome eight out of eight?

A. 'Buenos dias, muchachalatas!' ☐

B. 'I stole a kiss upon your cheek and now another kiss I seek!' 5

C. 'My mum thinks I'm awesome.' ☐

D. 'I will not do my business in this bucket! I am a lady!' 8

E. 'Kick back with a pound of bacon and enjoy the show.' 1

F. 'Ulch. People over thirty should really not make out.' ☐

G. 'Oh Gibby, there's so much not right about you.' 3

H. 'I may be an idiot but I'm not stupid.' ☐

iTwins

Freddie Benson scanned through the latest iCarly script and groaned. Carly and Sam were planning to finish this week's webisode with a cringeworthy prank clip. The other day they'd sent him an email saying that it was Clown Day at school. Guess who turned up to Ridgeway High wearing a comedy wig and out-sized shoes? Freddie had made a total fool of himself and Gibby had caught the whole thing on camera.

"Oooh, so funny," grouched Freddie, after the clip had run.

"Dude," grinned Sam. "You're the easiest person to trick ever!"

At least Carly looked more apologetic. "I feel really bad Freddie. So I'm giving you this one hundred dollar gift certificate to the Cheesecake Warehouse."

"Seriously?" smiled Freddie, peeking inside.

"Nah!" snorted Carly. "It's just lettuce!"

Sam high-fived her best friend – they'd got Benson once again!

At school the next morning, Freddie was still smarting from his double humiliation. It didn't help when Sam and Carly fell silent the minute he turned up at the lockers.

"What are you guys talking about?" he asked suspiciously.

Sam shot a 'don't-breathe-a-word-or-I'll-kill-you' glance at her friend.

"He's going to find out sooner or later," whispered Carly.

"Whatever," sighed Sam. "My sister's coming home for a few days and I'm peeved off about it, OK?"

Freddie rolled his eyes. This was the best scam yet! Sam fed him some story about a twin called Melanie going to a fancy boarding school on a scholarship, but he wasn't buying a single word!

"I'm not falling for it," he smirked, heading off to class.

Carly was working through some maths papers when Spencer walked in with the groceries.

"So what kind of homework are you doing?" he asked, shoving a pork roast into the fridge.

"I'm not," smiled Carly proudly. "I'm tutoring a kid that lives in our building."

Spencer was impressed – especially when his sister revealed the kid's dad was paying her good rates.

Suddenly a little voice piped up from the bathroom.

"Hey the soap in here smells awesome!"

The hairs on the back of Spencer's neck went vertical – Chuck Chambers! That devil-boy was his arch-nemesis and he was here, in his inner sanctum?

Chuck strolled into the kitchen and beamed at Carly.

"Chuck is evil!" hissed Spencer. "Once he tried to hit me with a racquet-ball racquet and then another time he locked me in the basement and squirted me with a suspicious liquid!"

CHUCK IS EVIL!

"I never did that stuff," said Chuck politely. Carly looked at Chuck's adorable little face. What was her brother talking about?

"You need to get a hot bath or something Spencer," she decided, turning back to her pupil. "Now let's check out your maths assignment for tomorrow."

Carly bent down to pick up a test paper from her rucksack, leaving man and boy unsupervised and face-to-face for a fleeting second. Chuck made the most of the opportunity, mouthing 'you're dead' across the kitchen.

"Carly!" bellowed Spencer.

Carly looked up, but Chuck was smiling sweetly again. What was wrong with Spencer today?

CAMERA FACE

<3

iTwins

Later, Carly and Spencer were slumped on the couch watching TV when Freddie called in to borrow some scissors. Even though he was in ninth grade, his mum kept a ban on dangerous stuff like that.

"Mel's on her way up," smiled Carly, buzzing Sam's sister in. "We're going to the cinema with Sam tonight."

Freddie darted a glare at Spencer. Had they got him in on it too?

The elevator doors opened and Mel (or was it Sam?) walked into the apartment. She was wearing a floral pink blouse and a pretty clip in hair. Very un-Puckett.

"Hey Mel!" cried Carly. "This is Freddie."

Mel flashed a lightbulb popping smile. "Hi! I recognise you from iCarly."

"Really?" scowled Freddie. "Isn't it convenient that Sam isn't here right now?"

"Clown Day." The guys were so busy wincing at Freddie's faux pas, they didn't hear the tiny creak coming from the kitchen.

Chuck Chambers crept out of the cupboard under the sink armed with a screwdriver and a utility belt. Whatever he was up to, it wasn't his maths assignment…

HOW CAN THEY THINK I'M THAT GULLIBLE?

"He thinks Sam's messing about having a twin sister," explained Carly. "I'll text Sam and tell her to meet us at the movie."

Things were getting awkward, but Freddie didn't care. He pulled a face as Mel stepped nervously back into the lift.

"How can they think I'm that gullible?" he asked Spencer when they'd gone.

Spencer only had two words to say to that.

Freddie was walking back across the hall to his apartment, when Sam strolled past.

"Impressive," he nodded. "So you changed your clothes and hair in the lobby and then took the main elevator back up here?"

Sam looked as if she didn't know what the chiz he was talking about. Unfortunately her phone beeped before she could call Freddie a nub.

"I've got to go and meet Carly and Mel at the Omniplex," she muttered, diving back down the stairs.

The next morning, Spencer staggered out to the kitchen to make some coffee. He swung open the larder door, and the whole thing came away in his hands! Worse was to come – when he tried to grab a juice from the fridge the door bounced onto his toe. Either Spencer didn't know his own strength or something fishy was going on.

"Hello," said an amused, high-pitched voice.

Spencer spun on his heels – Chuck Chambers! It all made sense. The tyke must have rigged the comedy doors up when he came over for his last coaching session with Carly. Now his arch-nemesis was standing here as bold as brass, a smug look plastered across his face.

"All right you little gremlin," roared Spencer. "You're in major trouble for this!"

Spencer made a lunge for Chuck, but the kid was far too quick for him. Chuck darted behind the counter and then pulled out a homemade super-soaker filled with brown slime.

"Ha ha!" cackled Chuck, spraying Spencer's hair and pyjamas. Thick brown liquid splattered across the kitchen tiles.

"Caaarlleeee!" shrieked Spencer, watching the little monster scramble out the front door.

Disgusted, Spencer gingerly used a finger to test the mysterious, chocolate-coloured goo. It was utterly gross.

"Ahhhh!" he choked. "Why did I have to do that?"

No matter what it took, Chuck Chambers would pay for this.

iTwins

"That would be really cool. I'd love to," she smiled. "Bye!"

Carly raised an eyebrow at Freddie as they watched Mel skip happily out of the door.

"I'm a genius," announced Fred. "Sam would rather chew broken glass than go on a date with me for a whole Saturday night. She'll never go through with it."

"You just asked Melanie," reminded Carly.

"You can pretend that if you like," said Freddie smugly. "But I know I'm going on a date with Sam."

It took a few seconds for the true horror of that final sentence to sink in.

"I'm going on a date with Sam!" he repeated, spitting smoothie all over the table.

While Spencer was scraping goo off his kitchen counters, Carly was sitting in the Groovy Smoothie with Sam.

"I thought you had detention today Puckett," said Freddie, sloping in to join them.

"She snuck out," replied Carly. "Apparently Miss Briggs only stays for the first five minutes. Melanie's just in the bathroom."

Freddie shook his head. This whole Melanie thing was getting boring now.

"I'll just wait here until the mythical 'Melanie' comes out," he replied.

Sam's Pearphone started to vibrate.

"Aw man!" she groaned. "Miss Briggs came back and saw that I ditched detention. I got to get back!"

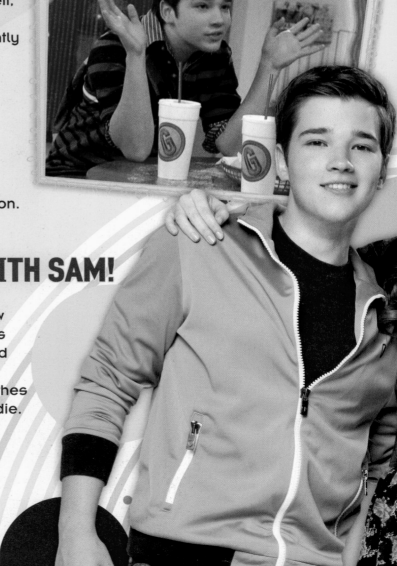

I'M GOING ON A DATE WITH SAM!

How convenient. Wasn't it interesting how Sam had to 'leave' every time Melanie was about to appear? True to form, Mel showed up two minutes later.

"I will say that you can change your clothes and hair pretty fast," acknowledged Freddie.

"I'm Melanie," insisted Melanie. "I really am Sam's sister."

"OK," challenged Freddie, pretending to play along. "How would you like to go on a date with me this Saturday?"

Melanie's face flushed with pleasure.

The moment that Carly's back was turned, Chuck grabbed Spencer by the hair and slung him across the coffee table.

"You listen to me," pleaded Spencer as the titch strong-armed him onto the rug. "I know what you are!"

Chuck didn't care in the slightest. He continued to batter his tutor's big brother until he heard Carly tripping back down the stairs. By the time she was back in the room, the snake was sat on the couch working out a tricky multiplication problem.

"Why are you on the floor Spencer?" asked Carly.

Chuck smiled innocently. "Maybe he had a stroke?"

Spencer leapt to his feet, looked daggers at Chuck and then dragged Carly upstairs. There was an open laptop waiting on a shelf on the landing.

"Socko leant this to me," he explained. "Along with some special software and a couple of teeny little secret video cameras. Take a look at what just

On Saturday evening, Chuck came over for his next tutoring session with Carly. The pair had only got through the first couple of questions when Spencer stalked in carrying a gunk-filled crash helmet.

"That little pimple filled my motorbike lid with chunky red goo!" he yelled.

Chuck looked up with fake concern. "You want me to get you a paper towel or something?"

Carly watched Spencer sneer at the kid and wondered why he was picking on him like this. She gave Chuck an affectionate pat and then headed upstairs to fetch the spare helmet.

HE'S EVIL,
AND I WANT REVENGE

happened downstairs."

Carly's eyes widened as the laptop played back a recording of Chuck's assault on Spencer.

"That lying little beast!" she whispered.

"You see!" spluttered Spencer.

"He's evil and I want revenge."

Carly knew just what to do. The little creep had a maths test coming up – it was time to tell him about a brand new number called 'derf'.

While Carly gave Chuck a taste of his own medicine, Freddie was out on his hot date with 'Melanie' at the coolest teen club in Seattle. Fred had to admit that Sam had really made an effort for this prank – she'd even brushed her hair and put on a girlie red dress.

"How long are you going to keep this up?" he asked. "Just admit you're Sam and we can leave." Melanie took a deep breath. "I would, but I'm not Sam."

"All right," schemed Freddie. "If you're not Sam, then I guess you wouldn't mind it if I held your hand."

Melanie giggled shyly, but she didn't take her hand away.

"I think you're really cute," she added.

"How can you say that without vomiting?" demanded Freddie. It was time to get nasty.

"If you're not Sam, I suppose you wouldn't mind slow-dancing with me." Melanie was up on the dancefloor in a flash.

"I like you," she whispered, pulling him into a clinch.

Freddie couldn't believe Sam was taking it this far! "You hate me," he gulped. "You always have."

Melanie shrugged.

"Maybe Sam hates you, but would she do this?" She leant forward and gave Freddie a lingering kiss on the lips.

"You swore we'd never do that again!" he gasped. Melanie just laughed. "I didn't swear anything."

Freddie's eyes were like saucers as his date leant in for another kiss. Sam was totally messing with his head! There was only one thing to do – run away…

The next day, Sam and Carly were having a game of indoor tennis when Chuck Chambers and his dad showed up at the front door.

"I just wanted to let you know we're not going to continue with the tutoring," explained Mr Chambers. "Chuck failed his maths test."

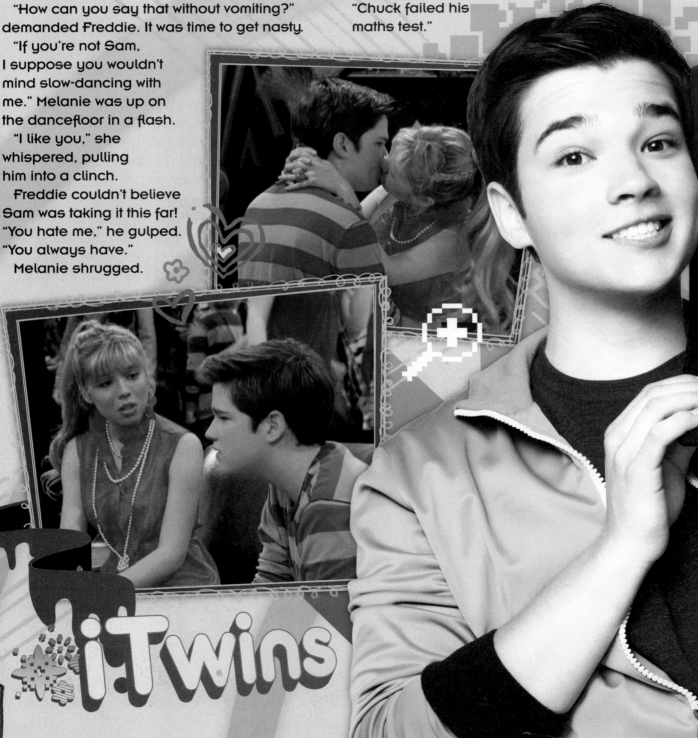

iTwins

"Oh… no," said Carly in mock surprise. Mr Chambers shot an exasperated look at his boy. "It's not your fault. He made up some fake number called 'derf'."

"I learnt it from her!" shrieked Chuck, jabbing a finger at Carly.

His dad smiled apologetically and then handed Chuck another three week's grounding. Before the pair could leave, Spencer popped his head round the door for a final word.

"When I had trouble with tests, my dad sent me to maths camp for the whole summer," he added. "You might want to have a look at this brochure."

Spencer whipped a flyer for 'Camp Addemup' out of his jeans pocket. "Thanks!" smiled Mr Chambers. "This looks perfect."

Chuck's jaw dropped at the prospect of three months working on algebra and long division.

"Enjoy your summer, Chuck," whispered Spencer.

The Chambers hadn't been gone for long, when Freddie popped in to return the Shay's scissors.

"You're here," he muttered, spotting Sam making herself comfortable on the couch.

"Yeah, like seeing your face freshens up my day," snarled Sam.

"You seemed to like my face last night," said Freddie. "When you had your lips all over it! I am not that gullible! I know there is no Melanie."

IN YOUR FACE, PUCKETT!

Carly stood up. "Yes, there…"

"Whoa!" yelled Sam, pulling her friend back down. "OK, you won. There's no Melanie, you're not gullible and you're too smart for me."

That was all Freddie wanted to hear. "In your face, Puckett!" he cheered, dancing out of the apartment. "Bye ladies."

Carly rolled her eyes. Why did all boys love to be right. She hoped he was happy now.

Ding! The elevator doors slid open and Melanie stuck her head out. "Hey!" she called. "Are we going to the mall?"

Sam and Carly grabbed their bags and jumped in the lift. "I can't believe you two are sisters," sighed Carly.

Sam and Melanie nodded sympathetically. "Me neither."

69

MY EVIL TWIN

Aaah, sisterly love! Someone to share smoothies, giggles and girlie goss with. Or not! Sam Puckett's twin Melanie is sweet, studious and always has clean hair, which in Sam's book is a disgusting combination of characteristics. What would your evil twin look like? Draw her (or him!) into the picture frame below.

·REC

Riddle It Right

Freddie has a hi-tech problem! He's been handed this fiendishly tricky riddle which hides the identity of an iCarly character. Use your iCarly knowledge to find the hidden person!

EACH LINE OF THE RIDDLE GIVES A CLUE TO A LETTER OR INITIAL. WRITE EACH ONE IN THE BOX AT THE END OF THE LINES OF VERSE. WHEN YOU'VE FINISHED YOU'LL REVEAL THE IDENTITY OF AN ICARLY CHARACTER.

1. My first is in Gibby, but not in Sam,

2. My second's in Puckett, but not in Pam,

3. My third starts the surname of Carly's worst foe,

4. My fourth is a fruity, cool lap-top to go,

5. My fifth starts Sam's answer when offered some grub,

6. My sixth sells nice pies, it's a shop, not a pub,

7. My seventh is the letter starting every show's name,

8. My eighth tops the Plaza where Carly found fame,

9. My ninth begins the tacos that Spencer makes,

10. My tenth precedes air when filming takes.

11. If you are baffled as to the final letter,

12. Begin a mean boy and you'll feel much better.

Bad PUBLiCiTY

Nevel Papperman is so unspeakably vain, he runs off stacks of new publicity shots every week to hand out to his fans. Every single one has been airbrushed, touched up and tampered with in a bid to make the reviewer look less uncool.

Freddie, Sam and Carly have decided to send up Nevel by running off some shots of their own. Never ones to take themselves too seriously, the guys have donned bunny ears and deeley boppers for the occasion!

This pile of pictures should all be identical — but there is one that doesn't quite match up to the rest. Draw a circle round the odd-shot-out.

WHO'S WHO HERE?

BFF

There are some crazy characters strolling round Seattle these days! Carly knows every single one of these lovable wackos, but what about you? Study each of the clues and then try and work out who's who. When you've sussed all six IDs write the names into the blank spaces.

1. **A LITTLE DUDE WHO SPENDS HIS DAYS TRYING TO TERRORISE SPENCER.**

_ _ _ _ _ _

2. **SAM'S DUBIOUS AND DELINQUENT MUM.**

_ _ _ _ _ _ _ _

3. **THE HEAD OF RIDGEWAY HIGH SCHOOL.**

_ _ _ _ _ _ _ _ _ _ _ _ _ _

4. **THE GROUCHY DOORMAN OF BUSHWELL PLAZA.**

_ _ _ _ _ _ _

5. **CARLY'S BAGPIPE-PLAYING ENGLISH TEACHER.**

_ _ _ _ _ _ _

6. **SPENCER'S CREATIVE BEST FRIEND.**

_ _ _ _ _

IF YOU WERE CAST AS A CHARACTER IN ICARLY, WHAT NAME WOULD YOU CHOOSE FOR YOURSELF?

....

....

....

IM PUZZLE

Carly, Sam, Freddie, Gibby and dotty iCarly fan Mandy are all trying to chat online, but there's a glitch in the system. The messages have got in a total jumble and no one knows who's saying what!

CAN YOU PUT THIS INSTANT MESSAGE STREAM IN THE CORRECT ORDER? WRITE THE CORRECT NUMBER NEXT TO EACH LINE.

CARLY: Cool beans. TTFN.

GIBBY: What about me?

SAM: Hey Gibby, Mandy's free.

FREDDIE: I'm having a Hawaiian. Just got to get my Mum to agree to put my bedtime back an hour.

SAM: That is so not happening.

MANDY: Wow, I'm totally having an IM with Carly and Sam! What time we meeting? I've got a wicked new duck mask to show you!

GIBBY: Did someone say pizza?

FREDDIE: Shut it, Puckett! C u at 6 Carly.

CARLY: Mandy – it sounds cool, but can we make it another time? Sam and I have got to work through some stuff for the show. Freddie, you in?

CARLY: Hey BFF, fancy picking up a Margarita from Omar's pizza tonight?

SAM: So lame...

SAM: I've already got a bucket of fried chicken on the go, but what the heck – I'm in Carls!

74

CUE, YOU!

Want to send a clip into iCarly.com, but don't know where to start? Tech producer Freddie has got all the information you need! Follow his golden rules and your video will stand a great chance of getting featured online (oh, as long as it's also side-splittingly, jaw-achingly funny!).

FREDDIE'S SUPER PRODUCER RULES

★ STAND CLOSE TO THE CAMERA, BUT NOT SO CLOSE THAT THE VIEWER CAN SEE YOUR NOSE HAIRS, JUST CLOSE ENOUGH THAT FOR THEM TO CAN SEE YOUR FACE.

★ SAY YOUR FIRST NAME AND YOUR AGE, THEN STEP BACK AND DO YOUR THING!

★ *Make sure your clothes don't have logos or bad words on them*

★ DON'T WEAR CLOTHES WITH THIN STRIPES.

★ *Don't say or do anything bad (nothing mean, no bad words).*

★ DON'T SAY OR SHOW FULL NAMES, SCHOOL NAMES, CITIES, STREET NAMES, PHONE NUMBERS, OR EMAIL ADDRESSES IN YOUR VIDEO.

★ TRY TO KEEP YOUR VIDEO SHORTER THAN THREE MINUTES.

★ *Watch your video before you send it in! Make sure it looks and sounds good. If it doesn't, try again and make it better.*

★ DON'T DO ANYTHING DANGEROUS. NO ONE WANTS YOU TO GET HURT IN THE NAME OF ICARLY!

★ YOUR VIDEOS SHOULDN'T INCLUDE MUSIC. BUT, IF YOU'RE SENDING IN A VIDEO OF YOU DANCING, AND YOU WANT TO INCLUDE MUSIC, THAT'S OK, JUST DON'T TALK DURING THE MUSIC.

★ ALWAYS MAKE AND KEEP YOUR OWN BACKUP OF YOUR VIDEO. THE CREW CAN'T SEND YOUR VIDEO BACK TO YOU.

GOT IT? GOOD! WHEN YOU'VE FILMED YOUR MASTERPIECE, CLICK ON HTTP://WWW.ICARLY.CO.UK/SENDSTUFF/INDEX.HTML AND UPLOAD!

APPLAUSE, PEOPLE!

POTTY PREDICTIONS

Whilst Spencer might rely on his magic meatball for guidance, Carly, Sam and Freddie are unsure what 2012 has in store for them. So here are some horoscopes that we reckon might come true for the trio... These may be potty predictions but silly things do happen! Predict some possibilities for yourself in the box below.

Sam will win the grand prize in a hot dog eating competition and then go home with a lorry load of wieners (wait, didn't that already happen?)

Carly will finally realise that Freddie Benson is the love of her life!

www.iCarly.com will welcome Lady Gaga, David Archuleta and Robert Pattinson as guest stars on the show!

My prediction for 2012 is ....
....
....
....
....

Answers

PAGE 8: LEWBERT'S LETTER LINK

```
    B E N S O N
      F E N C I N G
S T E V E N
S L I N E
    G A L A X Y W A R S
S C U L P T U R E
    R A N D O M
      P A M
      P L A Z A
W A D E C O L L I N S
    P R I N C I P A L
    S M O O T H I E S
  G R A V Y
  M A N D Y
```

PAGES 10-11: PUT IT TO THE TEST!

1. a 2. c 3. c 4. b 5. c 6. c 7. b 8. a
9. b 10. c 11. b 12. a 13. c 14. a 15. a
16. c 17. a 18. c 19. b 20. a

PAGES 18-19: STYLISH DOWN TO A TEE

FANTABULOUS FIVE!
a. SAM b. CARLY c. FREDDIE
d. FREDDIE AGAIN! e. SPENCER

PAGE 28: PILLOW MY HEAD!

1. GIBBY 2. SAM 3. CARLY 4. FREDDIE

PAGE 30: CARLY'S WORLD WORDSEARCH

```
M A B M S V D R H E
U S G I T R I S S K
C S R V K A D E I O
H I U B N S O C K O
A R G O S U C L C B
C A L P D A Z V U R
H M S B R I G G S A
A T U Y H C H U R E
L X M C S N I N F P
A Q O B A E N G U O
T B U L C V A U L X
A Q F F T E J N Y F
S B U R Y L L E B G
```

PAGES 38-39: START 2 FINISH

1. D iHurt Lewbert
2. G iEnrage Gibby
3. H iGive Away A Car
4. F iScream on Halloween
5. C iStakeout 6. E iLook Alike
7. B iHate Sam's Boyfriend
8. A iWant My Website Back

PAGE 57: HOT TO SPOT!

PAGES 60-61: PUTTING WORDS IN THEIR MOUTHS

1. E | 2. C | 3. G | 4. H
5. B | 6. A | 7. F | 8. D

PAGE 71: RIDDLE IT RIGHT

G
U
P [PAPPERMAN]
P [PEARPHONE]
Y [YES]
G [GALINI'S]
I
B [BUSHWELL]
S [SPAGHETTI]
O [ON]
N [NEVEL]

PAGE 72: BAD PUBLICITY

F

PAGE 73: WHO'S WHO HERE?

1. CHUCK CHAMBERS
2. PAM PUCKETT
3. PRINCIPAL FRANKLIN
4. LEWBERT 5. MS BRIGGS 6. SOCKO

PAGE 74: IM PUZZLE

1. Carly: Hey BFF, fancy picking up a Margarita from Omar's pizza tonight?

2. Sam: I've already got a bucket of fried chicken on the go, but what the heck – I'm in Carls!

3. Gibby: Did someone say pizza?

4. Mandy: Wow, I'm totally having an IM with Carly and Sam! What time we meeting? I've got a wicked new duck mask to show ya!

5. Sam: That is so not happening.

6. Carly: Mandy – it sounds cool, but can we make it another time? Sam and I have got to work through some stuff for the show. Freddie, you in?

7. Freddie: I'm having a Hawaiian. Just got to get my Mum to agree to put my bedtime back an hour.

8. Sam: So lame...

9. Freddie: Shut it, Puckett! C u at 6 Carly.

10. Carly: Cool beans. TTFN.

11. Gibby: What about me?

12. Sam: Hey Gibby, Mandy's free.